06/29/23

THE
FINAL MILE
HOME

TALES OF SELF DISCOVERY

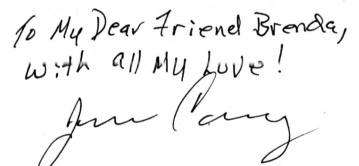

*To My Dear Friend Brenda,
with all My Love!*

JOHNNIE CALLOWAY

THE FINAL MILE HOME
TALES OF SELF DISCOVERY

Copyright © 2021 by Johnnie Calloway

ISBN: 9798703944721 (Paperback)

Printed in the United States of America

TABLE OF CONTENTS

Dedication

This book is written in dedication to my mom, who has been a spiritual inspiration for me my entire life, even in her physical absence.

Thanks, Momma

I AM THE AUTHOR OF
MY OWN LIFE.

❖

WHAT WILL I WRITE ON
THESE PAGES TODAY?

preface

I believe I have been a seeker all my life. I also believe all of us are, at least to some degree, seekers.

Unfortunately, most are seeking under the guidance of the ego, and the ego's tenet is, "Seek, but do not find." (A Course in Miracles text page 226). So we set out seeking inner peace in ways and places where it can not be found. Many seekers become either addicted to some substance or some other external means in an attempt to find inner peace. In other words, they try to fill an internal seeming void with an external, tangible means. It simply does not work.

The ego and fear are inseparable; in fact, they are the same. It is impossible to reach peace with fear as your guide. I personally have sought it through so many external methods that I can't list them all, but the most obvious are drugs, alcohol, women, relationships, gambling, and sex. Each of these just carried me farther into the darkened tunnel where the ego and It's fear rule.

There is a power in discernment, learning to determine the valuable from the valueless. We have all had idols in our lives, the things that we believe will make us whole, complete, and bring us fulfillment and peace. We collect and value trinkets; we use magical solutions to heal the seeming brokenness we think we have become.

These valueless trinkets, the cars, the houses, the money, the recognition will never give us what we are truly looking for. The acronym of alcohol-ISM is In Search of More. As is said in the twelve steps rooms, "One is too many, and a thousand is not enough."

For more than half of my life, I have been "Driven by a hundred forms of fear" (Alcoholics Anonymous page 62.) Through the Twelve Steps and A Course in Miracles (ACIM) teachings, I have discovered that most of my fears were unfounded.

In ACIM, on page 214, we read, "Children perceive frightening ghosts and monsters and dragons, and they are terrified. Yet if they ask someone they trust for the meaning of what they perceive and are willing to let their own interpretations go in favor of reality, their fear goes with them. When a child is helped to translate his 'ghost' into a curtain, his 'monster' into a shadow, and his 'dragon' into a dream, he is no longer afraid and laughs happily at his own fear."

I have learned, as a result of my own desperation, to look into the eyes of my own dragons and fears and face them with a strength that is not entirely my own. I have learned of the power the ego holds when we allow it to separate us from each other and our Source. I have also learned of the Power we have when connected, joined, and one. Still, our best attempts at joining take us to a place of being joined but in separate groups, in separate camps or pods. The question becomes, and the goal is: How to connect the groups, at least mentally? How do we, with all our differences and judgments, which we relish and even cherish, look beyond these and find the sameness we all share?

And last, but certainly not least, how do we find love for our brothers and sisters and our Source with a million judgments standing between us? Is it even possible that we can find peace in this war-riddled world? Well, I believe it is impossible not to.

Can I bring Love into a frightening world?

Can I, will I, rise above the fearful playground of the ego and shine a light where darkness seems to rule?

What can I give, and to whom?

Can I Love in the face of differences?

How important is it that I am right and others wrong?

Can I and will I forgive the "unforgivable," Love the unlovable, and seek peace among all this chaos?

These are the remaining questions we must ask.

How will you answer?

Notes

Part One

The Boy and the Dragon

There once was a boy, who more often than not, felt alone against the world. He lived as though there was a terrible beast out to get him as if a war was going on, and he was the only warrior in his army. There was an unseen dragon, ever on the alert, waiting for the boy to make a careless move. The boy had to learn to be quick of foot, evading the dragon at every turn, for he believed his very life was at stake.

The boy had to learn to deny his feelings, for feelings were a sign of weakness. If the dragon sensed any form of weakness, he would take it as an opportunity and breathe his fiery breath on the boy.

In the boy's nightmares, the dragon would take him in his sleep. So the boy could not afford to sleep. He would lie with one eye open and his ears ever on the alert for movement.

His senses were keen, and often he would know the dragon was coming before he even got close. The fear and anticipation at these times could take his breath. Even in these, the most terrifying of times, the boy's biggest challenge was staying aware enough to keep one step ahead of the dragon.

He had to be ever ready to do battle. He could not let the dragon know of his fear. It seemed as though fear just might be dragon food. Therefore the boy always wore protective shields that hid his fear. The dragon would have to be extremely sharp to catch this boy off guard.

This was especially so in other warriors' presence, for they appeared to be allies to the dragon, spies perhaps. So many times, the warriors had befriended him only to betray him; get close to him, then laugh when they breathed their fiery breath on him. And so he had learned, like a great actor, to play the role of a brave and mighty knight, though he was terrified within.

Often, in the most terrifying times, the boy would hear an unfamiliar and, therefore, frightening voice. But this was a gentle voice, with no grovel and no bark, though its message was just as frightening and foreign as was its tone.

"THERE'S MORE FOR YOU, SON. JUST HOLD ON."

He didn't trust the voice and chose to believe it was the dragon trying to deceive him. However, there was a small glimmer of hope with the voices' message, but even hope frightened him. Hope, you see, had always turned into disappointment, and his heart would become unbearably heavy and ache in immeasurable pain.

There was one place where the dragon did not seem to enter. In his adolescence, the boy had found a lake, a lake with beauty the eye could barely imagine. The water was so clear that the fish could be seen at great depths. There was a borderline of pine trees as tall as his young eye could see. The boy felt safe at the lake. He felt as though he were being held, perhaps even loved while at the lake. He imagined a sign at the entrance: DRAGON BEWARE. NO DRAGONS ALLOWED. The lake appeared to be his safe haven, a place where the weary boy could rest, even sleep, and take refuge from the dragon.

Normally, he lived in total silence, but while at the lake, he could speak freely of all the thoughts, he lived with daily, the thoughts that he dared not let anyone know. As the trees swayed gently, and the water sparkled gently, as if to encourage him, he could speak the truth about his troubles with the dragon. He spoke of how afraid he was and his worries of the dragons' victory over him. But outside of this place, his fears had to be kept secret or else; THE DRAGON MIGHT FIND OUT!

At the lake, the boy could also dream of a life he truly wanted. He dreamt of love and loved ones. Anywhere else, these dreams only angered the dragon, but here he felt safe to let his mind wander where it wanted.

He pretended he was a poet, a philosopher, even a great athlete—anything other than a tired, terrified, and beaten warrior fighting a hopeless battle.

Settled in this safe place, he could hear the gentleness of the voice that had frightened him so, and hear its wise thoughts:

"Often, in life, we are asked to face dragons, dragons so fierce that death itself seems more appealing. We must come to realize that it is only in facing these dragons that their fierceness will diminish. In doing so, we come to find our own inner strength."

But away from the lake, he continued with his troublesome life. As time passed, a young man now, and obsessed with the possibility of a battle, and his fear of the dragon, he had never allowed himself a true connection with a maiden. He could not trust maidens; they too, could be the dragon's spies. In times of depression and loneliness, he had attempted to find this connection, but these times only led to more self-doubt, confusion, and more loneliness. The maidens were inevitably wounded by his struggles with the dragon too.

He watched other warriors. They seemed to have beaten their dragons and taken on kingdoms and found maidens with which to share their lives. He felt cheated and alone. He felt singled out, isolated, with no sense of belonging, and he became very bitter. With no one to trust, no one with whom he could share his pain, his loneliness consumed him.

His obsession with the dragon, along with his loneliness, created an internal pain he thought he could not bear, and thoughts of taking his own life ensued. Yet even in these darkest of times, the voice would return with, "There's more for you, Son." Somehow these words, although frightening, also began to comfort him.

Still, his fear led him. His fear turned into anger and his anger into hatred. And the hatred only drove him deeper into the darkness of separation and isolation. Just as his world had become too dark to bear, a thought occurred to him.

'There has to be something more, something I cannot see. A reason, a purpose, a way to overcome all this pain, a way to overcome this ever-elusive dragon.'

He began to dream daily of finding someone to share his stories of the dragon and show the scars that no one had ever seen to share some of his pain. But the young man knew of no one he could trust as he feared, 'If they know, they will kill me.'

His preoccupation with conquering the dragon left him feeling exhausted and hopeless. As a result, he had neglected to take on the living responsibilities that other warriors now seemed to welcome, only enhancing his feelings of being an outsider.

So out of focus was he with the hunt that he did things on impulse, then wished he hadn't. He ran with warriors that knew no honor. He was torn between what was and what was to be. He had an inkling that he had been born to be a noble knight, yet he had been too consumed with protecting himself from the dragon to be concerned with things such as honor, pride, dignity, or honesty.

Still... Somewhere deep within, he had believed that his desire to be a noble knight would eventually make it so. He began to ask himself questions: 'Since my body is weak and exhausted from this never-ending battle, what if I try overcoming the dragon with intellect and heart?' 'What if I surrender?' And with that, he lay down his sword and took off his heavy protective shields and let himself be seen.

The warriors wondered how much of their lives had been wasted, trying to fight a dragon that only needed to be faced and not conquered. The young man wondered, 'Have I spent my entire life trying to conquer the unconquerable when all I could ever do was tame that which is definitely tamable?'

Together, the warriors began to hear that foreign voice of hope, the hope that had frightened them so with its softness and its gentleness. It now whispered,

"There is nothing to fear. There is no dragon, nothing to hunt, nothing to run from. It is the truth you have run from, and THAT TRUTH IS LOVE. Love is all that you have feared and fought."

There is a part of every human being.

that knows only love

And this is what we fear the most.

I once knew loneliness

To the point that it hurt

And I knew despair

To the point that I screamed

I lived in anger

To the point of rage

And I also knew hopelessness

To the point that I quit...

Then something happened

Why I don't know

A transition had started

So the real me could show

I heard a voice

Bringing me hope

A stillness had come

Bringing me peace

And somehow,

I knew

The war... was almost ... over

And...

There is a source of love within you
Meant to touch a heart
A ray of light you shine
That will always bring a smile
The power of God you own
That can heal all broken hearts
A part that knows of love
A love that you would hide
The spirit of love you are
From which you can't escape

If sometimes your dragon
Seems too fierce to stand and face alone
It might help to remember,
"You have never stood anywhere alone."

After finding the rooms of the Twelve Steps, I had finally discovered a true sense of hope. With hope came trust, and with trust came the courage to face all my demons. The power of connection and strength of knowing I was no longer alone in my battles nourished me, and I could begin to breathe without the pounding of my terrified heart.

Fear had always been my master. I had never had control of it. The elders led me to a deep internal investigation of ALL my fears, resulting from a thorough and fearless inventory. Connecting with these brave men and women gave me the strength to face the dragons of my life.

Notes

Part Two

Life in the Colony

Once upon a time, a delightful elves colony lived in a safe, prosperous, and enchanted land of Love. They worked, played, and most of all, they laughed together. At the core, very deep in this colony's heart, was a belief that connected each elf. "United, we can do all things, and all things are possible.'

The colony was an extension, or should I say an expression of "His Love." Oh, didn't I tell you?

"HE" IS THE GREAT ELF, THE ELF OF LIGHT.

Come with me to see this colony. It sits among soft rolling hills, blanket with maple trees that soar high into a sky as blue as sapphire. The lakes, rivers, and streams are all as clear as crystal. Grapevines cover the area with their natural sweetness, while flowers of every color are sprinkles here and there. And all of this is just for the beauty of it.

Here the days never end, and darkness never falls. There is no need for rain because life just lives naturally. There are no needs because all life is satisfying. There are no natural disasters. How could that which is natural ever be a disaster?

For the colony of elves, living in this wonderful place meant they knew no fear, for there was nothing to fear. There was an abundance of everything, and everything belonged to everyone; everything was shared freely.

GREED

did not exist.

Without greed, possession had no meaning. Me and mine were not even words in their vocabulary. This is why this place was so peaceful, for in it Love was all that existed, and in Love, all was given and received.

The elves' home was in the heart of the Great Elf. Being in His Heart, each elf knew its Source. They knew they had a common link: His all-embracing Love, which created an aura of Light around each elf. And so, enfolded in the Light of the Great Elf, the colony lived in peace.

United with each other, their home was called Heaven, a safe haven. It was a place created especially for the elves, where they could know and share each other's Love.

They knew that Heaven could never perish and that only what He created existed.

Monster of doubt

Then... one day one of the elves wandered astray and was kidnapped by the monster of doubt. The monster, having no birthplace, came from nowhere. It sprang up from thought, and fear was the essence of its being. With the elf's kidnapping, a once unknown fear and darkness fell over the colony, the elves became very tired, and soon the laughter they had always known was gone.

Following their weariness was a deep sleep, and in their slumber, they dreamt a dream that soon became a nightmare. The nightmare was one of division and separation, and they believed they would soon vanish. Their fear became terror.

They imagined each other as separate from the other, with separated needs and motives, with no momory of tho Light that oonnootod thom. Shortly thereafter, each elf was given a name, and now no two elves were the same. In this nightmare, once a world of abundance, now was a world based on lack. And so began their need for food, shelter, and rain for survival.

The animals and plant life, who had only been known as friends, became a food source. With the rain came floods and other natural disasters.

The most insane part of the colony's illusion was the belief that this was the Great Elf's handy work. It seemed to them that this was His plan. They even dreamed of rules and guidelines by which they would have to live to earn and know His Love. What they had once known as the Creator of Love, they now imagined as a destroyer of life, a vengeful and angry Creator who they now had to try to please and appease.

In their insanity, the elves imagined more and more rules and laws to follow. Not one elf could now be trusted. In their new world, they dreamed of elves that would lie, cheat, and steal. They dreamed they had been separated and divided in numbers too great to count. The concept of all one elf was lost.

Caught in this nightmare, the colony screamed in agony. Born in a world that knew no fear; they now felt trapped in their own terror.

In their dream...

They could see no hope, no way out.

They felt no Love for their fellow elves.

Their illusion seemed to last forever, and it

eventually came to represent eternity.

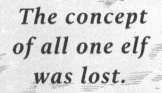

The concept
of all one elf
was lost.

Yet, somewhere, deep in their hearts, they questioned it all. The questions became the key to an unlocked door, and their minds began to open. The opening inspired a new hope of awakening from this nightmare. By reconnecting with the truth in their hearts, some of the elves imagined a savior, one meant to awaken them.

The Great Elf sent many enlightened ones to soothe the nightmare, but the elves had become so invested in the dream that they were now afraid of waking. Somehow they knew there must be a better way, but they were afraid to ask what it could be.

The monster of doubt had become their god, so they chose to believe in the darkness of doubt, which caused them to fear the Light. In this new world, the elves had created quite a paradox; a burning desire to awaken and a paralyzing fear of doing so.

Even when the Light came to their dream world, awakening appeared hopeless, and they seemed doomed. Lost in their dream, the colony forgot their created essence. They forgot the Great Elf created them and that all He created was Love. They forgot that Love is unchangeable and eternal, going on forever.

Then a wonderful thing happened! Certain elves began to look into the Light and awaken. Once awake, these elves began to speak of the insanity of the nightmares they all had shared. How odd it was that some of the elves who remained asleep had become so accustomed to the darkness that when these enlightened ones came to awaken them, they called them insane or even false prophets.

The awakened ones realized that they had forgotten there was nothing to fear in their dreaming. Even in their dream state, they had still been safe at home, merely dreaming in the Heart of the Great Elf. They remembered that they would always be united with all living creatures, all elves, a colony living in His Love in that still, quiet place. This was their gift, given by the Great Elf, the gift that can never be taken away.

No matter how frightening the master of doubt may seem,

Love was, and always will be, OUR reality.

Yes, OUR, you and I are the elves.
WE are the colony.
With our acceptance of our oneness begins
our awakening.
With our acceptance of the truth comes the
tremendous joy of reuniting and the
opportunity of sharing our Light for ALL to see.

PLEASE AWAKEN AND LET

YOUR LIGHT SHINE

THERE IS NOTHING TO FEAR

FOR THE GREAT ELF LOVE US

ALWAYS

I had listened to the ego's lies my entire life,
and unlearning its lessons became my
greatest challenge.
I had to learn to listen and listen to learn.

Misled and misguided

I followed a lie

Covered and shadowed

I thought I should die

Ignorant of silence

I thought I knew all

Too smart to listen

For my own quiet call

Deafened and silenced

Imprisoned in fear...

The screams were so frightening

That I never could hear

Fearful and frightened

The screams were so loud

Afraid of the light

That he hid behind clouds

Then awakened and hopeful

The truth never failed

Rejoiced and shouting

The spirit's unveiled

When you've lived your life
In darkness
Then the light becomes a source of fear.

I am the answer
To all that you've asked
And I am the teacher
Of all that you know
I have been sent
As your guide down the path
The one to awaken you
And restore you to light
Sent with a whisper
You are never alone
And I've come to take you
All the way home

If we always knew where our path leads...

There would be no need for trusting God.

Having learned the value
of connecting,
I needed to learn the power
of forgiveness.
I needed to learn to see all
similarities in myself and
those I tried so hard to keep
at bay. I had to learn to see
with a new pair of eyes, to see
the sameness in all.

What had true meaning, and what didn't?
What could truly nurture my soul, and what was
merely a distraction?
What would expedite my spiritual growth, and what
was a hindrance?

Notes

Part Three

The Evil King

There was once an evil king who ruled his kingdom with terror and rage. His subjects obeyed his every command for fear of his retaliation. Some were truly loyal to him, but even they never knew peace. He made up rules for all to live by, promising wealth and peace if they obeyed, but the rules could not be counted on because he would change them at any unexpected moment. On a whim, he would alter their existence and take everything from everyone he deemed had too much.

He was an insane king. There was no consistency in his behavior. He would go on killing sprees and order his soldiers to murder entire villages. He would order his wizards to cast magical spells making diseases that had no cure and all the while laughing at his victims' demise.

In the same breath, he could turn and show favor to others for no reason, granting them treasures beyond their belief, only to have them live in fear that he would take them away at any time.

He insisted on being praised, and anyone not obeying his demands would suffer, sometimes with great loss. The people in the kingdom tried their best to show their loyalty to him and showered him with compliments and gifts.

Even this was not enough for the evil king. He was vigilant for their worship, and still, sometimes, even those who honored his rules would have to pay the price of his rage.

Each day he walked the streets of his city, and as he passed his people, he insisted they greet him as "Your Majesty the King." The ones nearest to him as he passed by, had to bow and kiss his feet. Those who didn't comply were punished in ways that met his mood for the day.

One day, as the king was walking the streets, one small boy did not bow. Instead, the boy stood and looked upon the Evil King with a smile and simply said, "Hello." The king was enraged. With a scowl, the King, almost shouting, asked,

"Are you not aware of who I am and what I do to those who defy me?"

"Oh yes!" the boy said, still smiling. "It is because I know who you are that I am not frightened by you." The King let out what sounded like a growl and shouted to his guards, "Bring him! I will soon decide what to do with him".

The boy did not try to run, nor did he struggle to get away once the guards reached him. He astonished all onlookers by naturally and quietly taking their hands and walking away with them. As they walked behind the King, the boy was happily skipping and whistling.

Word was rushing through the kingdom of the boy whistling and skipping his way to certain death. Everyone was curious about the boy, and they came running to see him. The crowds grew and grew as the Evil King, and the whistling boy passed by. All who saw the boy smiled as he passed. Smiling itself was an oddity in the kingdom because their fear was too intense..

The King and his guards stopped as the King asked, "What is your name, boy?" The boy answered, "My friends call me In and all who know me call me friend and all who I know, I know as friend."

The King was very curious about this boy, who had no fear of him. He said, "I know you now, but I do not call you, friend." Giggling, the boy responded,

"You will, once you know me, as I already know you".

The King said, "So you think you know me?" "Of course I know you." the boy answered. "That is how I know that you cannot harm me, no more than I can harm you." The King replied, "If you know me, then you must also know of all the evil things I have done." "Yes, my friend, I know." the boy volleyed. "You know all the things I have done, and still you choose to call me friend?" asked the King.

"What I know," said the boy, "is that you want more than anything for your kingdom to love you, and you also want more than anything to love your kingdom. But you fear the love won't last and isn't real. Therefore, you attack out of fear, thinking that your attack is a show of strength and will keep the people of your kingdom from leaving you. You think your attacks will keep you safe. This is what I see in you; a frightened child, afraid of being left behind, rejected, and alone."

The King had never been spoken to by anyone in this manner, and although there was an urge to silence the boy, something inside himself encouraged him to listen. And so, to his own surprise, he did.

The boy continued,

"I see through your fears, your masks and your endless, pitiful displays of false power. I see you."

The King retorted, "Even knowing of my cruelties; still you forgive me?" To which the boy responded, "I never said I forgive you. What I am saying is I have never been upset with you. Therefore, forgiveness is not needed. To say I forgive you would say I have judged you. I cannot judge you."

The King thought for a moment and then said, "In is such a silly name. Where does it come from? What does it mean?" In chuckled and answered, "You cannot know it or understand it because of the armor of fear that you surround yourself with, blocking its meaning from your view."

"As I said, I do not need to forgive you because I have never been upset with you, but... you have been upset with yourself, and you still are. Once you have forgiven yourself and your people, then you will begin to understand the meaning of our name.

"How then, with such an evil past, could possibly forgive myself?" the King humbly asked. Cheerfully, In responded, " You are not bad. But you have been mistaken and are in need of correction. Look to me, to see yourself in me. Look to me, to see what you have worked so desperately to hide. Look to me to see how we are the same, both wanting more than anything to love and be loved. Look to me to disarm yourself and learn that only by choosing not to defend yourself will you ever know true safety."

The King was baffled. He did not understand In's words, but somehow they resonated as true for him, and he asked, "If I do this thing you ask and I see that we are the same, then I will understand the name, In?"

The boy quietly responded with great empathy, "Our name is so foreign and obscure to you that there is no way you could imagine what it means. It actually frightens you because you do not understand it. It is already within you. All you need do is reach within for the courage to see the truth, and it is there."

In continued, "You have no idea of the power of your truest desire. Want to be free of your fear, anger, and armor, more so than you want anything else. In wanting this, these things, along with your incessant need to be idolized, adored, and worshipped, will all slip away. Then, and only then, will the true meaning of our name be revealed to you."

So moved was he by the boy's words, the Evil King took off his crown and fell to his knees. With tears slowly rolling down his cheeks, he pleaded,

"Please, let me be free to become a friend to my people, to love them, and to see myself in them. Allow them to be free of my cruelty and to know me as a kindly King. Give me the strength to honor them as I have wanted them to honor me."

With this, In confidently went on, "The weakness you think you see in them is but a reflection of the weakness in yourself, that you have so wished to hide from anyone's sight, and most importantly from your own. Become determined to see them in their strength, and you will take off your armor, lower your sword, and send all your guards home."

In seeing their strength, you will see your own. Then you will know with a knowing that is beyond your comprehension, a safety that only those who share our name can know. And you will understand that all who live do indeed share our name, even though some, like you, have not remembered it yet. They will! And you can show them, as you learn it yourself."

The boy then smiled and continued, "Now you are ready to know our name. Our name is Innocence. Being Innocence, we can only know safety. Knowing we are safe, we cannot know fear. Without fear, we know we are loved, loving, and lovable. Knowing we are the essence of love, we discover a sense of peace within that is truly delightful!"

"See your people as you see yourself and discover the freedom that comes with forgivonooo ao tho woight of tho world io liftod from your shoulders. Realize a oneness with all that is, and know a sense of safety that you never dreamed possible. Learn of a childlike innocence that allows you to be the innocent man that you really are. Give yourself the laughter that you have envied and withheld from yourself for so long. Decide to see only love and pure joy will be yours. This can be your life, just for the choosing. In fact, it is already yours. Will you accept it, Your Majesty?" Followed with a chuckle.

And so the King stood and put his hand on the boys' shoulder and said, "Thank you, friend. Now let's go make friends with my people."

GO FORTH
IN LOVE, PEACE, AND LIGHT
MY FRIEND
YOUR FRIEND,
INNOCENCE

*Having
learned the value of
forgiveness, I had to discover
the importance of being
able to discern the valuable
from the valueless. And
remember my way home.*

Notes

Notes

Part Four

The Journey Home

Tired of his meaningless life, which led only to disappointment and depression, the young man set off on a quest. His life of collecting things had left him wanting. There had been no real fulfillment. There simply was never enough. There hadn't been enough cars, houses, relationships. Nothing filled the hole inside of him.

He knew there was more to life. He knew that peace and contentment were possible. The negativity of this life only prompted the question, "What am I missing?" He had read many books on the power of positive thinking and how it could change his life. So far, it was just information without application and only led to frustration. There had to be more! Even with all the reading, all the groups he had attended, all of the work he had done to grow, he was still left hungry.

Therefore, he packed the barest necessities; backpack, food, water, rifle, and knife and began his journey up the mountainside. At first, his pessimism ran amuck, and negativity ruled his mind. Yet, he was determined to see things differently. He was vigilant for the peace he sought.

At first, his thoughts went something like this;

———◁◆▷———

'Everything here is living, and all must kill to live. The oak tree outgrows the maple choking it off at the roots, and so the maple tree dies. The mountain lion feeds on the deer. The big fish eat the little fish, and the little fish eat bugs. On and on, it goes, and we call this survival (of the fittest). As for me? I utilize it all.'

The beauty I see in the oak means nothing to me when I need a fire. The shine I see in the bear's pelt has no value as I begin to feel the cold of winter. The grace I see in the antelope has no place in my heart when I know hunger. The joy I feel in loving loses meaning when I am in fear.

Is it beauty, when all things that live must die? Does everything always have to live with the fear of death? Even I, the most intelligent creature in these woods, must be alert. The bear, the mountain lion... they are capable of taking my life in an instant. Is nothing that lives ever to know safety? The mountain itself can take my life, even the weather. I must be forever watchful.

So must the people at the bottom of this mountain, seemingly safe in their homes. They have houses that protect them from weather, guns that protect them from wild animals and each other. As for me? I have my rifle and my knife at my side. Still, with all these things, I feel vulnerable to harm.

I know there is a Creator. Is He insane? Why would the creator of life create life just to watch it die? It makes no sense to me. There must be something I cannot see. All I see is pain, fear, and death. This Creator scares me. Has he created this world I live in out of boredom? Is all this a background for games He can play at His leisure? Can't He see all this suffering?

I see a young cub caught in a trap, screaming in agony, just to warm someone this winter with his fur. I see the mother bear powerless over the trap, crying for her young. Can't the Creator see this? Can't He stop it? He angers me with His game. I don't think it is fun. I see pain everywhere. I must escape from the pain. I must hide from Him and His stupid game. I know! I will refuse to play. I will stay on this mountain and eat plants and berries... I will no longer kill to live.'

The climb became more difficult, and the path more overgrown. Suddenly, he saw a path and realized there must have been others who had gone before him. He became determined to find them and ask what they knew of this Creator and His stupid game.

A newfound energy and hope accompanied him now, and his determination became fiercer than ever. Whoever it was who had gone ahead of him was leaving signs to follow, and he realized that if he slowed a bit, he was better at finding them.

The signs now seemed to be messages, each answering questions he didn't realize he had even asked. He wondered, 'Have these messages been here all along?'. Had he been blinded by his anger at the Creator to the point where he couldn't fully use his senses? Each of these messages were so foreign and profound.

The first stated, "You chose this path." He laughed, 'The one who goes ahead of me must be insane. Why would anyone choose to see all this pain and agony?' As he continued his climb, a thought occurred to him, 'Maybe I have needed to notice this pain to prompt the questions I need to ask.'

As his pace was now slower, he began to enjoy the journey more. He stopped to eat some berries, and on a branch, he found a note. "There is nothing to fear," it read. He read it over and over again. 'What of the lion, the bear? Surely I need to fear them.' He decided to sit for a moment with these thoughts. He realized that no matter how strange the messages were, they resonated with him as true.

Anxious to find answers, he heard these words whispered in the wind: 'The life you have been protecting is not the life you are.' Now totally confused and bewildered, he continued to relax and think.

It occurred to him that he had been climbing for days without food, without water, and he hadn't stopped once to sleep. Yet he felt no hunger, no thirst, and wasn't in the least bit tired. In fact, he felt vigilant. 'How can this be? All of these things are essential for life and energy?'

These insights themselves were now frightening him. They were the opposite of what the world below had taught. They were challenging his every belief. Still, there was a certain comfort in their ring of truth.

After a few days of reflection, his desire to learn pulled at him once again, and with much trepidation, he began to journey on. As he walked, he asked, "If the life I have been protecting is not the life I am, then who or what am I? Soon after asking the question, he spotted a tree with a carving on its trunk. As he got closer, he read this message: "The life you are needs no protection. The life you are can never die." He continued on his journey, feeling confused by this new thought yet simultaneously reassured.

As he walked on, it occurred to him that the days never ended, and night never came. This puzzled him somewhat; however, he started to get used to things on this mountain being a bit strange. Besides, he was too consumed by his new learning to pay too much attention to such things now.

"If the life I am can never die, then what am I?"

Immediately, the answer appeared scratched in the ground at his feet. "You are spirit. You are love." A chill ran up his spine, and goosebumps covered his body. These sensations were followed by a gentle warmth and a feeling of peace he had never experienced. He decided to be still and bask in these for a while.

As he sat with his back resting against a pine tree, he became aware that it was Spring! And that it had been for quite some time. Oh, how he loved the season! He took in the freshness of the air, the smell of the flowers blooming, and the colors of the dogwoods. Everything was so crisp and clean. As he thought back, he realized he had no idea how long it had been Spring. He had been so thoroughly engrossed in his plight for months.

He had once trudged along on this journey, not enjoying it at all, but now it brought him pure joy. He had lost all sense of time and had no idea how long he had been sitting. Only now, he realized he had seen no bear traps for quite some time. 'It must be too high up for trappers.' he thought.

As he stood, he noticed a Grizzly bear, and it had spotted him. Struck with a sudden sense of fear, he reached for his rifle. It wasn't there. He had left it behind when he had sworn he would not kill to eat. What could he do now? The bear was coming closer!

He remembered the messages:

'You chose this path.
There is nothing to fear.
The life you have been
protecting
is not the life you are.
The life you are can
never die.
You are spirit.
You are love.'

By now, the bear was upon him. I didn't appear to be angry, nor did it appear to be hungry. Instead, the bear nudged him with his nose and then snorted.

He was astonished! The bear had come to play! He surprised himself, for his fear was now gone. And so, he played with the bear. They wrestled and frolicked for hours. When he arose to look about again, he was amazed. Everywhere there were animals. Animals he had known to be prey one to the other...and now they were playing as though they were friends.

At the edge of the woods lay a mountain lion cuddled with a fawn. A badger was teasing a rabbit, and the elk and moose seemed to be playing tag. They all appeared to be in perfect harmony with each other. The sight brought tranquility and serenity that was new to him, yet somehow so natural.

'I could live here forever,' he thought. No more searching, no more learning, just being. But this place had prompted just one more question. "Where am I? "What is this place of joy and harmony?

He looked and listened for his answer. Nothing. He had learned just to ask again. The answer would come when he was ready to hear. So, he quickly asked again. "Where is this?" And a gentle wind answered to him through the trees.

Look about you, my son
And know that you are home.
Here there are no differences. All life is love.
Here there are no paths to choose, for they all
lead you home.
Here there is nothing to fear, for all things
come from love.
Here there is no life to protect because all life
is eternal.

———————◁♦▷———————

This place was created for you. It lives within you. The peace, harmony, and love that you experience here are within you. Remove the blocks that keep this from your awareness, and it is available to you every moment of every day.

MANY MILES, WE MUST TRAVEL.
TO LEARN THE LESSONS WE'VE
COME TO LEARN. STILL, THE
MILES CAN BE SHORTENED
AND THE LESSONS LEARNED. IF
WE RELEASE OURSELVES FROM
THE FEAR OF LEARNING THEM

Father, help me to see with Your eyes,
to hear with Your ears, to speak with
Your voice, to understand with Your
heart, and most of all Father help me
to live in Your Love.

Thank You

Notes

Notes

1

Have this

DRAGONS TO BUTTERFLIES

Exposing the darkness of child abuse
and giving "a voice to those kept silent
by fear, guilt, and shame."

LEARN MORE

2

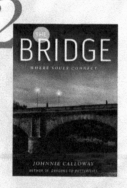

THE BRIDGE

A fictitious story about the real life, every
day pain of addiction and the bonds
created as a result of the connection of
spirit for those trying to stop.

LEARN MORE

3

Have this

THE LAST MILE HOME

Tales of self discovery

FOLLOW ME

For inspiration, updates, future
promotions and healing in general!

JohnnieCallowayAuthor

Johnnie Calloway

JohnnieCalloway_Author

MorphNew

JohnnieCalloway_Author

johnniecalloway.com

Follow Me

About the Author

Out of incredible desperation for his own healing and a deep need for forgiveness of himself and others, Johnnie Calloway became a seeker. His seeking led him to many spiritual teachings, books, classes, workshops, twelve-step programs, and ultimately A Course in Miracles.

His love of writing has been a large part of his own healing and his desire to help others has led him to share his writings. His three books "Dragons to Butterflies The Metamorphosis of A Man" "The Final Mile Home Tales of Self-Discovery" and "The Bridge Where Souls Connect" are his way of trying to give back what he feels has been so freely given to him.